HORRID HENRY
Runs Riot
Activity Book

Now a major TV series

Orion
Children's Books

Based on the HORRID HENRY books by Francesca Simon,
illustrated by Tony Ross

Horrid Henry Runs Riot

Could you be a member of Horrid Henry's Hotshots
or Moody Margaret's Mean Team?

Bet you want to be a high-scoring Hotshot, not one of Moody Margaret's smelly old Mean Team.

Join the magnificent Mean Team, not that bunch of losers!

SNIFF OUT THE STINKY TRAINERS

A number of stinky trainers are hidden
throughout this book.
Can you count how many?
You'll find the answer at the back of the book.

Top Teams

Who's in Horrid Henry's Hotshots and Moody Margaret's Mean Team? Fill in the criss-cross puzzle – all the Hotshots are filled in across and all the Mean Team members are down.

2 LETTERS
AL

4 LETTERS
BERT
JOSH

5 LETTERS
BRIAN
RALPH
HENRY
LINDA
SUSAN

6 LETTERS
GRAHAM
SORAYA
ANDREW

7 LETTERS
WILLIAM

8 LETTERS
GURINDER
MARGARET

CLUE:
Start with William.

Did you work out the two teams?

Fill in their names below:
HORRID HENRY'S HOTSHOTS:

_____

_____

MOODY MARGARET'S MEAN TEAM:

_____

_____

Henry's Howler

Follow the instructions below then read the leftover letters from left to right to find the answer to Horrid Henry's Howler:

HENRY: Why couldn't the car play football?

F	C	I	P	R	S	K	T	M
M	W	J	X	O	Q	Q	Z	X
N	J	F	X	C	S	J	X	L
K	S	R	Y	S	P	H	R	F
A	P	K	Z	D	Q	W	Z	Q
F	X	O	W	J	M	N	K	F
K	E	C	J	S	B	W	X	J
F	Q	M	O	P	X	S	O	Q
J	C	M	S	T	P	Z	M	C

Cross out 5 Cs
Cross out 6 Fs
Cross out 7 Js
Cross out 5 Ks
Cross out 6 Ms
Cross out 5 Ps
Cross out 6 Qs
Cross out 3 Rs
Cross out 7 Ss
Cross out 4 Ws
Cross out 7 Xs
Cross out 4 Zs

ANSWER:

— —   — — — —   — — —   — — — —

Tangled Tennis Strings

Someone from the Mean Team has been tampering with Al's tennis racquet. Follow the strings and find out who.

Crazy Cricket

Henry discovers there are ten ways to be out in cricket. Find all ten by starting from the red letter, then moving up, down or sideways, but not diagonally, to find a winding track. At the end, you'll find a four letter word that reveals the number of runs Henry scores!

CAUGHT
STUMPED
RUN OUT
BOWLED
LEG BEFORE WICKET
TIMED OUT
HANDLED THE BALL
HIT WICKET
OBSTRUCTED THE FIELDER
HIT THE BALL TWICE

START

C	M	P	B	O	A	L	E	D	T	H
A	U	E	T	W	B	L	T	I	F	E
U	T	D	U	L	E	H	C	E	L	D
G	S	R	O	E	H	I	U	H	R	E
H	T	U	N	D	T	T	R	I	T	W
E	B	G	E	L	D	W	T	T	L	I
F	O	R	E	W	E	I	S	T	L	C
T	E	K	C	I	L	C	B	H	A	E
T	E	D	T	H	D	K	O	E	B	D
I	M	O	U	A	N	E	T	K	C	U

END

Henry scored a

___ ___ ___ ___

HENRY'S HOWLERS

What animal is best at hitting a cricket ball?

A bat.

Sporty Spot the Pairs

Aerobic Al loves running fast, even when it's time for a break.
Can you spot the three matching pairs in the six pictures below?

The three pairs are:

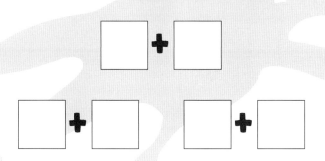

What's harder to catch the faster you run?

Your breath.

Find the Footballs

Find your way from the beginning of the maze to the end. See if you can pass ten lost footballs on the way, without retracing your steps.

START

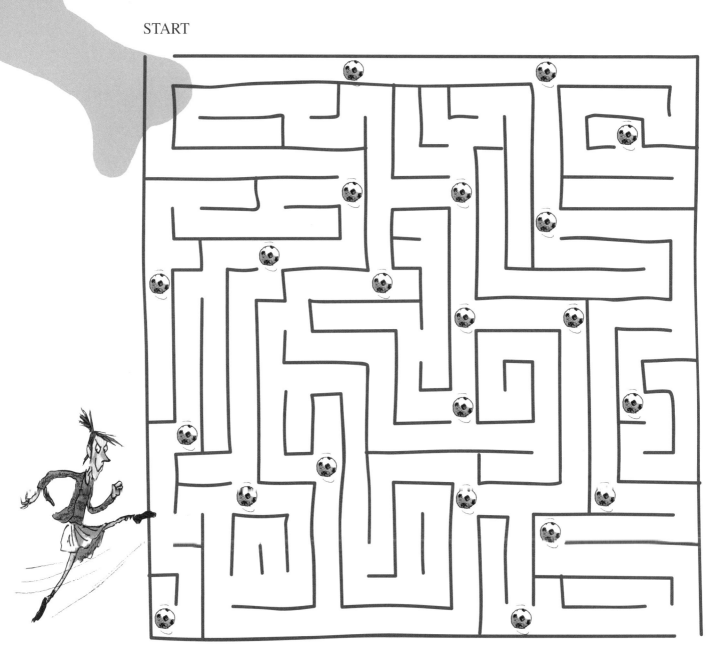

END

Sporty Silhouettes

Can you match the eight members of Henry's class to the silhouettes below?

ANSWERS:

1.___ 2.___ 3.___ 4.___ 5.___ 6.___ 7.___

Criss-cross Tricks

Horrid Henry dreams of being able to do all sorts of skateboarding tricks. Can you fit them all into the criss-cross puzzle?

4 LETTERS
POGO

5 LETTERS
OLLIE
GRIND
PIVOT

7 LETTERS
WHEELIE
SWEEPER

8 LETTERS
BACKFLIP
NOSEGRAB
WALLRIDE

9 LETTERS
HANDSTAND
FOOTPLANT
SPACEWALK

11 LETTERS
MONSTERWALK

CLUE:
Start with the longest and shortest words!

Football Fun

Henry is using all his skills – elbowing, barging, pushing and shoving – to win the game. See if you can spot where the ball should be on each of these four pictures. Draw an X to mark the spot.

Team Trials

It's time to try out for the Hotshots and the Mean Team. Take the Team Tests, and write your Hotshot scores in the blue boxes and your Mean Team scores in the red boxes.

WORD COUNT

How many three or four letter words can you write down, using the letters in the words chosen by the two team captains?

**Horrid Henry's
Hotshot Word:**

BADMINTON

**Moody Margaret's
Mean Team Word:**

ACROBATIC

Write your words down here (if you run out of space, use a piece of paper)

_____	_____	_____	_____
_____	_____	_____	_____
_____	_____	_____	_____
_____	_____	_____	_____

How many did you find? Write your scores in the boxes:

HOTSHOTS [ ]   MEAN TEAM [ ]

Football Figures

How many goals have the Hotshots and the Mean Team scored this year? Fill in the missing numbers. The number in each ball is the total of the two numbers below it.

HOTSHOTS

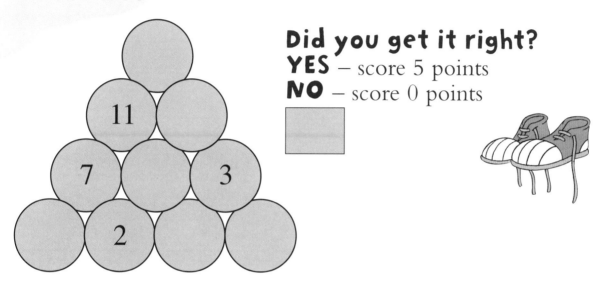

Did you get it right?
YES – score 5 points
NO – score 0 points

MEAN TEAM

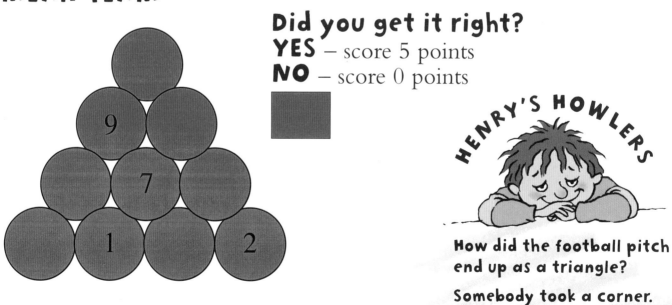

Did you get it right?
YES – score 5 points
NO – score 0 points

HENRY'S HOWLERS

How did the football pitch end up as a triangle?

Somebody took a corner.

Hotshots' Football Challenge

Help the Hotshots find all the football words in the wordsearch. From the first thirteen left over letters, find out who's the best footballer in Henry's class.

CAPTAIN
DEFENDER
GOAL
KICK
MIDFIELD
PITCH
SIDELINE
CENTRE
DRIBBLE
GOALIE
MANAGER
OFFSIDE
REFEREE
STRIKER
CORNER
FOUL
HEADER
MATCH
PASS
SAVE
TACKLE

E	M	O	S	O	R	D	M	L	U	O	F
Y	D	S	M	E	E	I	A	A	R	G	A
H	A	I	D	R	D	E	N	T	U	G	J
P	C	A	S	F	N	I	A	T	P	A	C
R	E	T	I	F	E	N	G	T	E	E	S
H	E	E	I	I	F	L	E	E	N	I	D
H	L	K	L	P	E	O	R	T	D	T	R
D	C	A	I	S	D	E	R	E	X	A	I
S	O	T	A	R	F	E	L	Z	R	C	B
G	Q	V	A	E	T	I	K	I	C	K	B
N	E	T	R	M	N	S	G	O	A	L	L
B	T	U	R	E	N	R	O	C	P	E	E

The best player in Horrid Henry's class is

_ _ _ _ _ _   _ _ _ _ _ _ _ _

Score ten points if you found all the words, and another five if you found the hidden name. Write your score in the box.

14

The Mean Team's Awful Athletics

Lazy Linda always has an excuse to get out of Games. Find the athletic activities in the wordsearch, and spell out Linda's excuse using the first seventeen left over letters.

CLUE: The two-word athletic activities appear as one word in the wordsearch.

E	S	E	L	D	R	U	H	I	S	M	Y
S	S	C	H	A	I	R	E	P	D	R	P
P	O	A	F	I	H	S	R	E	T	I	O
G	M	H	H	T	G	I	C	N	S	G	L
N	R	U	O	C	N	H	U	U	V	V	E
I	O	H	J	T	E	O	J	R	S	S	V
L	T	H	P	G	C	L	E	U	B	B	A
E	O	D	T	S	N	M	P	D	M	H	U
V	H	H	S	A	M	O	E	E	G	P	L
A	S	O	O	A	R	A	L	O	E	N	T
J	R	P	H	K	A	A	Q	B	Y	T	B
C	U	V	D	E	O	V	M	O	X	T	S

CROSS COUNTRY
HIGH JUMP
LONG JUMP
SHOT
DISCUS
HURDLES
MARATHON
SPRINT
HAMMER
JAVELIN
POLE VAULT
STEEPLECHASE

Linda's excuse

— — — — — — — — — — — — — — — —
,

Score ten points if you found all the words, and another five if you found the hidden name. Write your score in the box.

Hotshots' Quiz

It's time to test out your knowledge in the two rival quizzes. Answer the questions and add up your score.

1. **About how far do you have to run in a marathon?**
   (a) 6 miles   (b) 16 miles   (c) 26 miles   **Answer: ___**

2. **Where will the Olympics be held in 2012?**
   (a) London   (b) New York   (c) Athens   **Answer: ___**

3. **Henry imagines he is the greatest footballer who ever lived. What does he call himself?**
   (a) High-Header Henry (b) Hot-Foot Henry (c) Hotshot Henry
   Answer: ___

4. **Why does Horrid Henry hate his swimming lessons?**
   (a) He hates water (b) He's scared of drowning
   (c) He's scared of Soggy Sid   **Answer: ___**

5. **When Horrid Henry's class play football to win two tickets to a football match, who does Miss Battle-Axe choose as man of the match?**
   (a) Moody Margaret   (b) Aerobic Al   (c) herself   **Answer: ___**

6. **Who wins the cross-country run at Horrid Henry's school sports' day?**
   (a) Beefy Bert (b) Horrid Henry (c) Aerobic Al   **Answer: ___**

Total score: [ ]

Mean Team Quiz

1. **How many events are there in a decathlon?**
   (a) 1 (b) 10 (c) 5   **Answer:** ___

2. **If you finished second at the Olympic games, which medal would you win?**
   (a) Bronze   (b) Gold   (c) Silver   **Answer:** ___

3. **Who is the best footballer in Horrid Henry's class?**
   (a) Aerobic Al (b) Beefy Bert (c) Moody Margaret   **Answer:** ___

4. **Why does Moody Margaret stay at Horrid Henry's house?**
   (a) Her parents have gone on holiday
   (b) Henry's parents have invited her for a sleepover
   (c) Her bedroom is being redecorating with
       a 'pirate' theme   **Answer:** ___

5. **Why does Moody Margaret buy Perfect Peter at Horrid Henry's jumble sale?**
   (a) She feels sorry for him with Henry with as his brother
   (b) She wants a slave
   (c) To raise money for Children in Need   **Answer:** ___

6. **On Sports' Day, who is Moody Margaret's partner in the three-legged race?**
   (a) Sour Susan (b) Horrid Henry (c) Lazy Linda
   Answer: ___

Total score:

Sporting Sudoku

Fill in the boxes so that each one contains a football, a tennis racquet, a cricket bat and a hockey stick. Don't forget – every row across and column down must contain all four pictures too!

HOTSHOT SUDOKU

Did you get it right?
YES? Score 10 points
NO? Score 0 points

MEAN TEAM SUDOKU

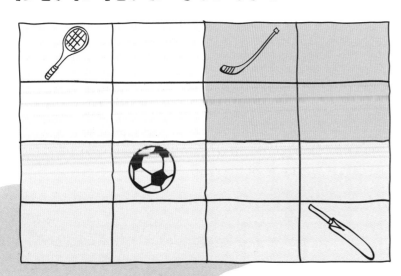

Did you get it right?
YES? Score 10 points
NO? Score 0 points

Super-league Sudoku

The teams have joined together to create the toughest test of all.
Fill it in so that every row, column and coloured box contains
all the numbers 1–6.

5			◯		
		6	1		3
	5	2	◯	4	◯
1			2		
	4		3		
6		1			4

CLUE: find the three numbers in the circles first.

TEAM SCORES

It's time to find out if you scored better on Horrid Henry's Hotshot Trials or Moody Margaret's Mean Team Try-Outs.

HOTSHOTS: Add up all your scores in the **BLUE** boxes. **GRAND TOTAL =**

MEAN TEAM: Add up all your scores in the **RED** boxes. **GRAND TOTAL =**

HOTSHOTS

Is your top score in the **BLUE** box? Welcome to the **HOTSHOTS!** With Horrid Henry's tripping tactics, Aerobic Al's speed and Brainy Brian's smart strategies, the **HOTSHOTS** are always on the ball. Gorgeous Gurinder takes a perfect penalty, while Jolly Josh and Rude Ralph's antics keep up the team spirit.

MEAN TEAM

If your top score is in the **RED** box, welcome to the **MEAN TEAM!** With Moody Margaret on side, this team is always in with a chance. She's not only the best player in the class – she's the second best and the third best too! Greedy Graham is great in goal and Sour Susan is surprisingly speedy. Beefy Bert is a top tackler – but sometimes he does forget which team he's on!

Swimming Stars

It's time for you to relax and do some cool pool puzzles!

Aerobic Al, Greedy Graham and Moody Margaret all win medals in the swimming competition. Can you work out who is competing in which race, and which medals they won?

RACES: backstroke, crawl, butterfly
MEDALS: gold, silver and bronze

	RACE	POSITION
AEROBIC AL		
GREEDY GRAHAM		
MOODY MARGARET		

Clues

1. Moody Margaret didn't do as well in her race as Greedy Graham did in his
2. Greedy Graham did the backstroke
3. The person who did the butterfly came first

20

Clockwords

Horrid Henry's hates swimming. Follow the time instructions and write the letters in the answer spaces to find out what Henry tells Soggy Sid to try and get out of his lesson.

Where does the big hand go when it's...
1. Quarter past eight
2. Ten to nine
3. Twenty-five to nine
4. Half past eight
5. Twenty past eight
6. Quarter to nine
7. Five past eight
8. Ten to nine
9. Twenty-five to nine
10. Twenty-five past eight
11. Twenty-five past eight
12. Nine o'clock
13. Five to nine
14. Five past eight

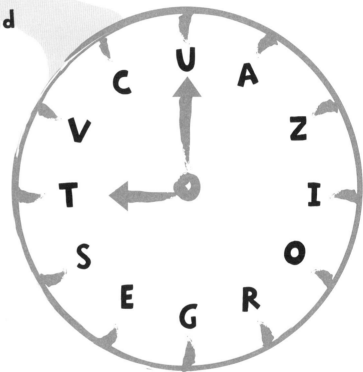

ANSWER:

__ ' __ __   __ __ __   __

__ __ __ __ __ __ __

21

Hurray for the Hotshots

Henry and his team are celebrating a Hotshot win.
Can you spot the eight differences between the two pictures?

Write your answers here:

1. _____
2. _____
3. _____
4. _____

5. _____
6. _____
7. _____
8. _____

Swimming Costume Crossword

Complete the crossword by answering the questions about this picture.

CLUES
Across:
1. What is painted on the wall?
4. Which character has a hairy chest?
5. What colour is Sour Susan's swimming costume?
6. What is Aerobic Al wearing on his feet?
9. What is the colour of the stars on Rude Ralph's trunks?
10. Who has forgotten his swimming things?

Down:
1. What is Soggy Sid wearing around his neck?
2. What colour are Greedy Graham's trunks?
3. How many children are wearing goggles?
7. What is Henry's brother called?
8. How many boys are standing in the row?

Answers

page 2
There are 8 stinky trainers hidden throughout the book.

page 3

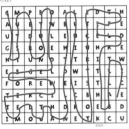

HOTSHOTS: Henry, Josh, Andrew, Gurinder, Brian, William, Al and Ralph
MEAN TEAM: Margaret, Linda, Graham, Susan, Bert and Soraya

page 4
IT ONLY HAD ONE BOOT!

page 5
Soraya

page 6

Henry scored a DUCK!

page 7
A and E, B and C, D and F

page 8

page 9
1 = D   2 = E   3 = B   4 = F
5 = A   6 = C   7 = G

page 10

page 11

page 12
Here are some words you might have found:

BADMINTON
3-letter words: BAD, BAN, BAT, BID, BIN, BIT, AID, AND, ANT, DAB, DIM, DIN, DOT, MAD, MAN, MAT, MOB, NAN, NIB, NIT, NOD, NOT
4-letter words: BAND, BOND, BIND, DINT, MOAN, MOAT, TOAD, MINT

ACROBATIC
3-letter words: ACT, ARC, AIR, CAR, CAB, CAT, RAT, ROT, ROB, RIB, OAT, OAR, BAR, BAT, BIT, TAR
4-letter words: CART, COAT, CRIB, CRAB, BOAT, BRAT, BOAR

page 13
Hotshots: 18 **Mean Team**: 24

page 14

The best player is: MOODY MARGARET

page 15

Linda's excuse: I'M SCARED OF HEIGHTS

page 16
1. c   2. a   3. b   4. a
5. c   6. b

page 17
1. b   2. c   3. c   4. a
5. b   6. b

page 18

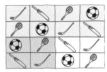 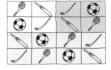

page 19

page 20

	RACE	POSITION
AEROBIC AL	BUTTERFLY	GOLD
GREEDY GRAHAM	BACKSTROKE	SILVER
MOODY MARGARET	CRAWL	BRONZE

page 21
I'VE GOT A VERRUCA

page 22
The differences are:
1. Mrs Oddbod's glasses are darker
2. Miss Lovely's eyebrow is missing
3. There is an extra cup on the table
4. Henry has black socks
5. The cloud is missing
6. Moody Margaret has white shorts
7. Anxious Andrew has blond hair
8. Aerobic Al's t-shirt has a different coloured neck line

page 23

24